CAPED CRUSADER CLASSICS

JUDGE DREDD GRAPHIC PAPERBACKS

versus

The Penguin

TITAN BOOKS

THE CHARACTER OF BATMAN WAS CREATED BY

BATMAN vs THE PENGUIN
ISBN 1 85286 093 6

Published by
Titan Books Ltd
58 St Giles High Street
London WC2H 8LH

First Titan Edition October 1988
10 9 8 7 6 5 4 3 2

Cover designed by Rian Hughes

Printed by Cox & Wyman Ltd, Reading, Berkshire.

Yes...IT'S TRUE! THAT FABULOUS BIRDMAN, THE PENGUIN, IS GIVING UP BIRDS! FOR ONE THING, HE'S TIRED OF BEING A JAIL-BIRD! BUT DOES THIS MEAN THE PENGUIN HAS REFORMED? WELL, HARDLY... FOR DON'T FORGET THAT THE PENGUIN IS ALSO KNOWN AS "THE MAN OF 1,000 UMBRELLAS," AND WHEN HE SETS HIMSELF UP IN THE UMBRELLA BUSINESS, IT MEANS BATMAN AND ROBIN HAVE TO TANGLE WITH...

the PARASOLS of PLUNDER

BATMAN ENDORSES PENGUIN UMBRELLAS

BANK

WHAT NEW BUSINESS DOES THE PENGUIN MEAN? SOME WEEKS LATER, AT THE HOME OF SOCIALITE BRUCE WAYNE AND HIS WARD, DICK GRAYSON...

FROM BIRDS TO UMBRELLAS! SEEMS THE PENGUIN'S DROPPED ONE OF HIS CRIME TECHNIQUES ONLY TO CONCENTRATE ON ANOTHER!

HMM... THE PAROLE BOARD DIDN'T SAY HE COULDN'T USE UMBRELLAS. IT MIGHT BE LEGITIMATE. STILL, BATMAN AND ROBIN OUGHT TO CHECK!

PENGUIN UMBRELLAS, INC... PLAN RECORD PRODUCTION AFTER REFORMED ARCH-CROOK ACQUIRES PLANT

SO, LATER THAT DAY, IN A STREAMLINED PLANT...

SO... YOU'VE COME TO CHECK UP ON ME, EH? WELL, GO AHEAD! I'M PRODUCING THE FINEST UMBRELLA ON THE MARKET... WITH MORE STEEL THAN ANY OTHER BRAND! STRONG AND DURABLE!

AND NO TRICK UMBRELLAS, I HOPE!

SHORTLY AFTER, IN THE OFFICE OF POLICE COMMISSIONER GORDON...

MR. RINK, HERE, IS NIGHT WATCHMAN OF THE COLE BANK BUILDING. FOR 3 NIGHTS RUNNING, HE'S SEEN A MYSTERIOUS HELICOPTER LOWER A MASKED FIGURE TO THE ROOF IN AN ADJOINING BUILDING. BUT THERE'S BEEN NO ROBBERY...NOTHING!

ALL WE FOUND WERE FOOTPRINTS ON THE ROOF AND THIS OUTLINE OF THE BAT-SIGNAL SCRATCHED IN THE TAR! HAVE YOU ANY IDEA WHAT'S BEHIND IT?

MAYBE SOMEONE'S TRYING TO CONTACT ME SECRETLY. ANYWAY... THERE'S ONE WAY OF FINDING OUT!

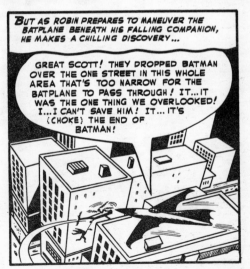

BUT, IN THE FINANCIAL DISTRICT, THE DAY PASSES WITHOUT MISHAP, AND AS DICK, BRUCE AND A BUSINESS PARTNER PREPARE TO LEAVE THE OFFICE...

IT'S STARTING TO RAIN. BUT SINCE I BOUGHT TWO OF THESE WONDERFUL PENGUIN UMBRELLAS THIS MORNING, BEFORE THEY WERE ALL SNATCHED UP, I CAN LEND YOU ONE, BRUCE!

ER...UH... THANKS...

AND SO, ONTO A STREET FILLED WITH PENGUIN UMBRELLAS AS A RESULT OF BATMAN'S ENDORSEMENT COUPLED WITH THE THREAT OF RAIN...

THE PENGUIN SURE DID ALL RIGHT USING BATMAN IN HIS AD!

SAY, BRUCE... MY WATCH IS OFF. HAVE YOU THE TIME?

THAT'S ODD! MY WATCH IS OFF, TOO!

AS THE SWITCH IS CLOSED, THE PENGUIN'S UMBRELLAS, SPOTTED ALONG THE BEACH, BEGIN TO SPIN...

AND AS THE DUST STORM INCREASES IN TEMPO, THE PENGUIN AND HIS MEN, PROTECTED BY MASKS, CLOSE IN ON THE BEACH CLUB...

QUICK, MEN... WITH A SAND UMBRELLA TO COVER US FROM THE BATPLANE, LOOTING THE BEACH CLUB WHILE THE GUARDS ARE TOO BLINDED TO STOP US, SHOULD ONLY TAKE A FEW MOMENTS!

DOWN IN THEIR SECRET **BAT-CAVE**, THE TWO UNDERGO A SWIFT CHANGE OF GARB...

SOON AFTER, IN THE OFFICE OF POLICE COMMISSIONER GORDON...

SURE ENOUGH, HIGH ABOVE...

BATMAN AND ROBIN! I DIDN'T EXPECT YOU SO SOON!

YOU MIGHT AS WELL SURRENDER, PENGUIN-- THIS IS AS FAR AS YOU CAN GO!

BUT THE MAN OF 1,000 UMBRELLAS HAS OTHER PLANS, AS HE LEAPS FROM HIS PERCH, AND...

SORRY TO DISAPPOINT YOU, BATMAN-- BUT MY PARACHUTE-UMBRELLA CAN TAKE ME DOWN SAFELY! TA-TA!

LATER, BACK IN HIS HIDEOUT...

TOO BAD THAT PESKY *BATMAN* HAD TO SPOIL SUCH A PERFECT CRIME-- BUT I'LL HATCH ANOTHER! WHICH EGG-- WHICH EGG, I WONDER, WILL INSPIRE MY NEXT CRIME?

I WISH THIS MYSTERY EGG WOULD HATCH SO THAT I CAN SEE THE TYPE OF BIRD THAT EMERGES! THE SUSPENSE IS ALMOST UNBEARABLE!

HMM... THIS EGG HATCHED A *HERRING GULL!*

DOES THAT SPECIES HAVE ANY PARTICULAR TRAIT?

THE ANSWER COMES SOON ENOUGH, AS A RUGGED HELI-
COPTER DESCENDS TOWARDS THE TOP FLOOR OF A
SKYSCRAPER...

NEXT INSTANT, AN INGENIOUS MECHANICAL "CLAW"
REACHES INTO THE OFFICE AND CLAMPS ABOUT
A SMALL SAFE...

As LUCK WOULD HAVE IT, THE CRIES ATTRACT *BATMAN* AND *ROBIN*...

THERE, *THE PENGUIN'S* "GULL" CRIME! THAT 'COPTER WILL PROBABLY DROP THE SAFE DOWN ON THE ROCKS AND CRACK IT OPEN, THE WAY GULLS CRACK CLAM SHELLS!

COME ON, *ROBIN*... WITH THIS SAND TRUCK, WE'LL BE ABLE TO FOLLOW THAT PLANE AND MAYBE THWART THE CRIME, TOO!

UPON TRAILING THE 'COPTER'S FLIGHT TO THE END OF TOWN...

LOOK-- THERE'S *THE PENGUIN!*

HE'S SIGNALLED THEM TO DROP THE SAFE SO IT'LL CRACK OPEN ON THAT ROCK-- BUT HE'S DUE FOR A DISAPPOINTMENT! HANG ON, *ROBIN*...

GUNNING THE MOTOR, *BATMAN* PITS THE TRUCK IN A RACE AGAINST THE PLUNGING SAFE...

AND, JUST IN THE NICK OF TIME...

BAH! **BATMAN'S** BEATEN ME AGAIN!

WHUMP

A QUICK SIGNAL TO THE PLANE, AND *THE PENGUIN* MANAGES ANOTHER AIRBORNE ESCAPE BEFORE THE LAWMEN CAN REACH HIM...

TALLY HO, **BATMAN!** I'M HITCHING A RIDE TODAY SO I CAN HATCH A CRIME TOMORROW!

WELL--AT LEAST HE'S GOING OFF EMPTY-HANDED AGAIN!

LATER... ONE OF THE OTHER EGGS IS HATCHING, BUT THE MYSTERY EGG IS STILL INTACT! BY JOVE, I DO WISH IT WOULD HURRY UP AND REVEAL ITS SECRET!

SHORTLY AFTERWARD, IN A GREAT HALL HOUSING THE *GOTHAM LIGHT AND POWER SHOW*...

AND HERE WE HAVE A SCALE MODEL SHOWING HOW WATERFALLS SUPPLY POWER FOR ELECTRICITY...

EXHIBIT E

AT THAT MOMENT, IN A BASEMENT ROOM THAT REGULATES THE WATER PIPES...

NOW WATCH WHAT HAPPENS WHEN I DUMP THIS CHEMICAL CONCENTRATE INTO THE PIPE THAT FEEDS THE "WATERFALL"!

LIKE TWIN HAWKS, THEY POUNCE ON THEIR QUARRY...
THAT DOES IT... NOW WE CAN GO AFTER THE PENGUIN!

AS THE **DYNAMIC DUO** CHASES *THE PENGUIN* DOWN A CORRIDOR...

HE'S GONE THROUGH A DOOR-- BUT WHICH ONE?

THAT CRAZY LAUGH OF HIS IS COMING FROM THERE! LET'S GO!

HEE! HAW! HAW! HEE! HAW! HAW!

BUT AS THEY DASH INTO THE ROOM...

IT'S EMPTY! BUT THAT BIRD...!!

THE AUSTRALIAN *KUKIBURRA*, SOMETIMES CALLED THE *LAUGHING JACKASS*-- PLANTED HERE BEFOREHAND BY *THE PENGUIN!* HE DELIBERATELY IMITATED ITS LAUGH, IN CASE HE HAD TO MAKE A FAST ESCAPE!

HEE! HEE! HAW! HEE! HAW! HAW!

THE END

IT MEANS A FLOCK OF TROUBLE FOR *BATMAN* AND *ROBIN* WHEN THAT POMPOUS LITTLE BIRD-BANDIT, *THE PENGUIN*, GOES INTO ACTION AGAIN.' BUT THIS TIME THE CROOK OF 1,000 UMBRELLAS IS BENT ON LEGENDARY LARCENY, SINCE IT'S BIRDS OF *FABLE* HE USES FOR CUNNING CRIME.' AND WHEN THE *BASILISK* AND THE *PHOENIX* AND THE *THUNDERBIRD* FLY OUT OF FOLKLORE INTO TODAY, THERE'S NOTHING MYTHICAL ABOUT THE MENACE OF...

"The Penguin's Fabulous Fowls!"

THE RELEASE OF A NOTORIOUS CONVICT BRINGS FAMED CRIME-FIGHTERS *BATMAN* AND *ROBIN* ON A SPECIAL VISIT TO STATE PRISON...

YES, *THE PENGUIN* IS BEING RELEASED TODAY, AND HE SAYS HE'S REALLY GOING STRAIGHT THIS TIME! HE'S BEEN STUDYING UP SOME PROJECT ABOUT BIRDS!

OH, OH-- THAT'S NOT SO GOOD, WARDEN! WHEN THE PENGUIN RIDES HIS BIRD HOBBY, IT'S USUALLY FOR *CRIME!*

BUT THE LITTLE BIRD-BANDIT SEEMS IN EARNEST ABOUT REFORM THIS TIME...

YES, *BATMAN*, I'M THROUGH WITH CRIME! SOON I SHALL ASTOUND THE WORLD IN A LEGAL MANNER! MY VAST KNOWLEDGE OF BIRD LORE CONVINCES ME THAT MANY FABULOUS BIRDS OF THE PAST-- THE *PHOENIX*, THE *BASILISK*, AND SO ON REALLY EXISTED!

BUT THAT'S IMPOSSIBLE, PENGUIN!

SO THE PENGUIN DROPS OUT OF SIGHT, WHILE *BATMAN* AND *ROBIN* IN THEIR EVERYDAY IDENTITIES OF WEALTHY BRUCE WAYNE AND HIS YOUNG WARD DICK GRAYSON, GET A WELCOME REST...

THE PENGUIN HAS JUST ARRIVED AT GOTHAM CITY HARBOR IN A CHARTERED SCHOONER AND HAS PROMISED TO MAKE A SENSATIONAL ANNOUNCEMENT!

I KNEW THIS QUIET WAS TO GOOD TO LAST! GET INTO YOUR COSTUME, DICK... IT'S UP TO *BATMAN* AND *ROBIN* TO FIND OUT WHAT THAT LITTLE SCHEMER IS PLANNING NOW!

AND IT'S INDEED A SENSATIONAL ANNOUNCEMENT THAT GREETS THE TWO LAWMEN WHEN THEY REACH THE DOCK...

YES, GENTLEMEN, I'VE SUCCEEDED IN MY QUEST FOR THE BIRDS OF LEGEND! THE *ROC*, THE *PHOENIX*... I HAVE SPECIMENS OF THEM ALL IN THESE SPECIAL AIR-CONDITIONED CASES!

BUT THOSE BIRDS WERE ALWAYS CONSIDERED MYTHICAL! LET'S SEE ONE OF THEM!

BASILISK

PHOENIX

⑦

WAIT A MINUTE-- HE *IS* FLYING! THAT'S NOT *BATMAN*... IT'S SOME SORT OF BATLIKE CREATURE... A *MAN-BAT!*

IT'S GHASTLY! RUN!

WHILE IN THE SECRET *BAT-CAVE* BENEATH THE WAYNE MANSION...

ROBIN, YOU TAKE THE *BAT-PLANE* AND PATROL THE SKY FOR THE PENGUIN'S BIRDS... I'LL USE THE *BATMOBILE* ON THE GROUND, AND CALL YOU BY BELT-RADIO IF I NEED YOU!

GOOD IDEA, *BATMAN!*

BUT **BATMAN**, FOR THE FIRST TIME, SOON FINDS THE PEOPLE OF GOTHAM CITY FLEEING FROM HIM IN TERROR!

RUN! IT'S THAT AWFUL **MAN-BAT!** GET AWAY!

MAN-BAT? SO THAT'S THE MYSTERY BIRD THE PENGUIN THREATENED ME WITH? IT **COULD** DESTROY MY CAREER, BY MAKING PEOPLE AFRAID OF ME WHEREVER I APPEAR!

AT THAT INSTANT, FROM HIGH IN THE SKY, COMES A TENSE CALL BY BELT-RADIO...

BATMAN, THERE'S A WEIRD MAN-LIKE BIRD FLYING OVER 9TH AVENUE!

I'LL STOP THAT **MAN-BAT!** YOU SWOOP DOWN AND LAND ON THE TERMINAL ROOF!

IMMEDIATELY, *BATMAN* RACES TO THE TOP OF A TALL SKYSCRAPER, AND...

SMACK!

THE ONLY WAY TO STOP THIS THING IS BY FORCING IT DOWN TO THE GROUND!

AND BY THE TIME *ROBIN* JOINS HIM...

SO THAT'S THE ANSWER. A *MECHANICAL*, MONSTROUS MAN-BAT!

RIGHT... *ALL* THE PENGUIN'S BIRDS ARE MECHANICAL FAKES--THE "THUNDERBIRD" THAT DREW LIGHTNING AND CARRIED AWAY THE ART-LOOT, THE "PHOENIX" WHICH FLEW AWAY WITH THE BANK-CASH, AND THE "BASILISK" THAT PRODUCED KNOCKOUT GAS!

THEN, AS THEY RENEW THEIR PURSUIT OF THE **PENGUIN** . . .

LATER, AT POLICE HEADQUARTERS, *BATMAN* TELLS NEWS REPORTERS OF THE *PENGUIN'S* RETURN TO CRIME...

BATMAN, WE'RE ALL ROOTING FOR YOU! YOU'LL GET THAT LITTLE BUZZARD YET!

I HOPE SO!

AMONG THE GROUP IS *VICKI VALE* NOTED NEWS PHOTOGRAPHER, AND *BATMAN'S* DEVOTED ADMIRER...

AFTER THE *PENGUIN* SERVED HIS LAST JAIL TERM, HE WENT INTO RETIREMENT! WHY DID HE SUDDENLY GO BACK TO CRIME NOW?

VICKI, I WISH I KNEW..

PRECIOUS MINUTES ARE LOST BEFORE *BATMAN* AND *ROBIN* FREE THEMSELVES AND PURSUE THE GIANT FLYING "PENGUIN"...

ROBIN-- LOOK OUT! THE *PENGUIN'S* STEERING THE BLIMP'S "BEAK" RIGHT AT YOU!

DESPERATELY, *ROBIN* SENDS HIS *WHIRLY-BAT* DIVING--BUT DOESN'T QUITE MAKE IT!

THAT STEEL "BEAK" SHATTERED THE PROPELLER! *ROBIN* WILL PLUNGE TO THE GROUND! I'LL NEVER REACH HIM IN TIME!

SUDDENLY, SENSING IMMINENT DANGER, *BATMAN* DROPS BEHIND COVER--AND JUST IN TIME!

THE CONCUSSION WOULD HAVE FLATTENED ME! THE *PENGUIN* DROPPED THAT FIGURE LIKE A DECOY DUCK--AND SENT ME ON A WILD GOOSE CHASE!

BOOOM!

LATER, WHEN *BATMAN* FLIES TO THE COLLAPSED BLIMP...

ROBIN-- ARE YOU OKAY? WHAT HAPPENED?

WHEN THE BLIMP LANDED, I TRIED TO TAKE ON THE *PENGUIN* AND HIS TWO STOOGES-- BUT THE *PENGUIN* CLOUTED ME WITH HIS UMBRELLA!

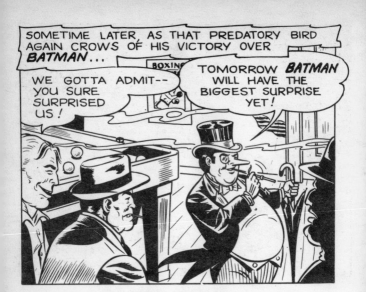

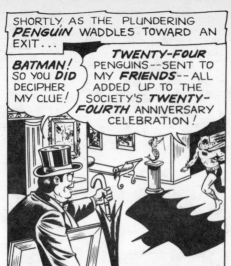

The End